NICOLE MOSS

90/-

NICOLE MOSS

HOW THE ZEBRA GOT ITS STRIPES

A collection of stories and pictures
by the children of Kenya
With an introduction
by Richard Leakey

Alan Hutchison, London

First published 1978 by Alan Hutchison
Publishing Co. Ltd., 2, Logan Mews,
London W8 6QP.
© Alan Hutchison Publishing Co. Ltd.,
ISBN 0 905885 01 5
All rights reserved
Design by Valerie Sargent
Stories and paintings collected in Kenya
by Sandra Price
Printed in England by
Sir Joseph Causton & Sons Ltd.,
London and Eastleigh
Cover picture by Margaret Kelly,
Loreto Convent, Nairobi

INTRODUCTION

Most people in the world have been exposed to animal stories at one time or another during their childhood and it does seem to be a universal feature of human cultural experience. Certainly, animal fables go back throughout the period of recorded history and it is likely that prehistoric man was a great story teller on the theme of animals. Our relationship to other animals is extremely important and many ideas and morals can be put across to younger people through the use of tales about familiar animals.

The stories published here were gathered by children in response to a suggestion from the staff of the Wildlife Clubs of Kenya Headquarters. It was proposed that the children should talk to their elders in the school holidays and bring back the tales so obtained for submission to the Clubs' offices. About 300 stories were sent in; these were sorted and the best ones were summarised in brief paragraphs for circulation to all the Clubs again as a theme for a National Art Competition.

The best stories and art are reproduced in this book and it is especially pleasing to note that many of the tales are those that have been handed down over many generations and form an important part of Africa's rich cultural heritage. It is interesting to find close parallels between some of the contemporary African tales and the famed AESOPS FABLES which were first told more than 2,500 years ago by Aesops, an African also, who had been sold into slavery in ancient Greece.

Having been associated with the Wildlife Clubs of Kenya since the organisation began, it gives me great pleasure to see this book in print and I hope that others will get pleasure from reading and re-reading the various stories. The authors of the contributions will be delighted with the knowledge that their efforts have given happiness and understanding to fellow humans in the far corners of our earth.

Richard E. Leakey has been associated with the Wildlife Clubs of Kenya Association since its inception in 1968, serving as Chairman of the Wildlife Clubs of Kenya Council.
Best known for his work in the field of prehistory, and particularly for dating the origins of man, Mr. Leakey is also deeply involved in several areas of wildlife conservation:– wildlife education, policy making and active campaigning for wiser use of wildlife resources in East Africa.
For the past 10 years, he has held the post of Director of the National Museums of Kenya.

CONTENTS

THE STORY
OF THE
GUINEA-FOWL

A guinea-fowl is a game bird with dark grey feathers spotted with white
which many people look at with immense admiration, but few try to
probe into the way in which these feathers got their wonderful
colouration. It is for this reason that I am writing about the relationship
between the guinea-fowl and other animals and circumstances that led
to the "painting of its feathers."

Legend has it that long ago when
animals had freedom to do things the way they liked, the guinea-fowl dwelt in
the plains where there was little interference. It had many allies, chief among them
was the cow, but the buffalo, elephant and buck were also its friends. On the enemy
side were the lion, rhinoceros and the eagle, whose assaults kept the guinea-fowl
under constant fear. On more occasions than one the bird visited its allies, sometimes
to ask for aid and advice about how to achieve a prolonged period of peace. At other
times it went only to chat and to joke.

On one bright summer morning the guinea-fowl decided to pay the cow a visit.
But on its arrival at the cow's home it met the biggest calf looking after a younger
one; the cow was on the rear side of the homestead settling a dispute with the lion.
They had been there for a long time without coming to a conclusion and this only
helped to increase the lion's anger. There was silence and no movement—nothing
except for the thumping of their large hearts. Then suddenly the lion sprang onto
the shoulders of the cow and started to dig in its claws. The cow mooed in agony,
not knowing what to do.

While this was going on the guinea-fowl was talking to the calves in the house
when the moos and the lion's roars shattered the peace and quiet. The bird went out
to see the state of affairs and the sight of the struggle clotted the blood in its veins.
It stood there in a dilemma not knowing whether to run away or to help the cow
against the lion. Then, almost instinctively, it turned its back to the centre of the

scene and started digging large amounts of soil with its feet and throwing dirt into the eyes of the enemy. In a shorter time than it takes to tell, the lion was down on his knees pleading for mercy as its eyes were blocked with soil so that it was both difficult to see and very painful. This gave a chance to the cow to take revenge and she kicked the lion. Then to draw the life out of this big bully the cow used its horns to stab the lion's chest, straight to the heart and that was the end of it!

An unearthly silence overcame the scene and it was now time for the cow to thank the guinea-fowl, for had it not been for the bird's timely help the cow and her calves would all have lost their lives into the hands of the bloodthirsty Mr. Lion, "King of the Beasts."

"It is really a great day," started the cow, "and this has marked a milestone in our friendship. I've no appropriate words with which to thank you but I will do a little thing for you, a thing that will differentiate you from the rest of the birds and at the same time, I am sure, will give you great pride."

"Thank you very much," said the guinea-fowl, inwardly very pleased with himself.

The cow went into the house and brought out a pail which she filled with milk from her udder. Then, instructing the bird to stand very still, she dipped her tail into the pail and started to sprinkle milk on the feathers of the bird. The bird became beautiful with white spots evenly distributed over its feathers. This seemed the crowning moment of the guinea-fowl's whole life.

When the ceremony was ended, the guinea-fowl went home, escorted part of the way by the cow. Out of complete generosity and common sense did the bird help the cow from the murderous lion, and in return beauty was placed on its feathers which for a long time had been only plain coloured. "A friend in need, is a friend indeed."

By David Magoma
Agoro Sare High School, Kisii
Picture by Azmeena Rajan
Highlands School, Eldoret

HOW THE ZEBRA GOT ITS STRIPES

A Maasai Legend

Along time ago, Zebras and Donkeys were brothers and sisters. They came from one mother and one father. In those days all the animals were friendly and they lived together. They had no king, no queen or any leader. If they wanted to say anything, they all informed each other.

One day they had a meeting and decided it was time to choose a leader. They all had different opinions or ideas of how to choose one. Every animal tried to give its own idea, but there were so many animals that it stretched into several days of meetings.

On the third day, Mr. Hare's idea was among the best. His suggestion was that all animals with horns should choose their leader, and those with claws would choose their leader. In two days' time a feast would be held to introduce the new leaders. There were also prizes to be won by the most beautiful animals.

The Zebra and his brother Donkey saw that they would win the prizes. They decided to beautify one another, but the problem was that the Zebra wanted to be beautified first, and so did the Donkey. They called in Mr. Hare for a decision, since he was a well-known judge and very clever. When he came he decided that Zebra should be first because he was the elder brother of Donkey. Therefore, the Donkey started beautifying the Zebra. He coloured Zebra with thick stripes of black and white, very slowly and carefully. By the time Zebra was being finished, the other animals started to move towards the feast.

As soon as the Zebra was finished, he ran to the rest of the animals, and left his brother Donkey un-beautified! Angrily, the Donkey tried to decorate himself, but failed, and this is why he has so few colours today.

The Zebra won a prize and to this day is liked because of his beautiful skin. But from that time the Donkey and Zebra did not meet, nor stay together, nor make any friendship again.

By Willie E. Shukoky
Narok Secondary School
Picture by Peggy Mullama
Limuru Girls' School

THE FABLE
OF
ONJINYO

When I was very young I used to listen to stories told by Grandmother.
She is no longer alive but her stories still ring in my ears as if I had only
heard them yesterday.
"Why did you try to kill that beautiful and innocent bird? Do you even
know how it got its beautiful colour?" These were the questions my
Grandmother asked me when she saw me trying to kill a bird which only
just escaped. My answer was silence which indicated to her that I did
not know, so she told me this story.
"The name of the bird is Onjinyo, the wagtail, and this name means
beautifully decorated," she said. This is the story of how he got his
colouring.

A long time ago this bird was black all over
his body and the white stripes which now give it its beautiful colour were not there.
One day the Elephant gave a very big feast to which he invited all the birds. Almost
every bird went and in respect they all tried to look smart and attractive.

Onjinyo was also there and as usual appeared very dull and clumsy in his black
coat. This made all the other birds laugh at him at the meal. In fact they threatened
him so badly that he decided to go and live with man instead of amongst his fellows
who did not enjoy his company. This idea caused much laughter among the other
birds who told him that he would make a good supper for man as soon as he arrived.
However, he stuck to his decision and set off on his long journey.

After flying for a long time he reached a certain house but there was nobody there.
He went into the house thinking that he would find someone inside, but even the
house was empty. However, in one corner he found some white maize flour in a
basket. He wondered what it was so he tasted it and found it tasteless. But suddenly
he thought of how the other birds had laughed and despised him because of his
black colour. With this thought in mind he decided to dip himself into the flour so
that his body could turn white like the flour.

At this moment the owner of the house returned and was surprised to find him there—and to make it worse, in the flour. The woman got hold of him and at first thought of killing him but as the customs of our society prohibit the killing of any bird or animal in the house, she spared him and he flew away praising the woman for her kindness.

The body of this bird has remained white, especially the lower section which had stayed in the flour for a long time but the back lost some of the flour during the flight. When I asked my Grandmother why the rain did not wash away the flour from the bird she told me the flour was magic.

The wagtail promised not to eat anything belonging to people from then on as the woman had shown him such mercy. The bird also decided to stay near people and that is why wagtails are usually found around houses or on the roof. This is why my Grandmother told me not to kill it because it does not do any harm to man. The wagtail has kept its promise since that time and so I have taken a keen interest in this bird whenever I have seen it around.

By David Magoma
Agoro Sare High School, Kisii
Picture by Peter Jalamgo
Kokure Secondary School

HOW THE DOG CAME TO LIVE WITH MAN

Long, long ago, the dog is said to have been living in the forest with other animals. Then how did it come to live with man?

In those times, the dog was brother to the jackal, and they lived together happily.

It happened that there was a very cold month so that every animal was shivering day and night. The dog and his brother, the jackal, used to sit on the high rocks to watch every part of the land. But soon they could no longer stay on the rocks. They went into a cave where they found other animals suffering because of coldness.

Because they were not related to these other animals, they were sent away. The dog and his brother ran from one rock to another but they could not settle anywhere because it was so cold.

At last, the jackal said to his brother dog, "Look here, my brother, we cannot die of coldness here. The people in the village always have fire, so I request you to run to one of the houses, and steal some fire when they are not looking."

Hearing this, the dog was both pleased and annoyed. He asked the jackal, "How shall I get the fire, and what will happen to me if the village people see me?"

The jackal told the dog how he would do it and the dog left when the sun was setting.

Arriving in the village, the dog found all the people asleep. Not only that, but he was surprised to find that the people had killed a cow yesterday and a lot of meat and bones were thrown everywhere. He immediately started to eat as quickly as he could, but even so he could not finish all he found there. Satisfied at last, he forgot why he had come to the village in the first place. Going round the village, he found a kitchen which was warm and comfortable, and slept there.

In the morning the owner of the kitchen came and was surprised to find a wild animal sleeping so peacefully. At that moment the dog awoke and saw the woman at the door. "I shall not show any fear or any sort of cunning to this woman," the dog thought to himself, "otherwise she will call other people and I'll be killed. I shall keep cool and watch."

Seeing the animal was not afraid nor vicious, the woman took some meat from the pot and threw it to the animal. The dog ate the meat, happily wagging its tail. The woman called people to come and see the animal which did not fear people. They were surprised and also showed no fear, and they never harmed it. They let it alone.

As for the dog, he was no longer thinking about his brother, the jackal, but about the kindness and tenderness he was being shown by the people. He was remembering the coldness of the rocks, compared to this place of peace, where he was given free food without hunting for it, as he had to in the forest.

He started speaking to himself, "How can I leave all these things and these kind people to return to the forest? The other animals do not allow us in the caves, and to get food is a difficult task. There is no fire to warm our bodies. I shall never go back to that place if these people go on treating me as kindly as they are doing."

Throughout the next day, people came to see the dog, and when they gave it any sort of food, the dog ate it, and they were really interested in its behaviour. They said, "The animal must not be disturbed, and we shall see what will happen next."

In the forest, the cold had grown worse and worse. The dog's brother, the jackal, was very worried about the dog. He waited and waited, but saw no sign of the dog.

When he could bear it no longer, he decided to wait until nightfall and go near the village to look for his brother.

When night came, the jackal started going slowly towards the village. He was careful not to be seen by the people. When he was about two hundred yards away, he stopped and listened. He heard only the voices of people, but nothing else. He stood on a rock and called, "Dog, Dog!"

The dog caught the voice of his brother and remembered what he had been sent to the village for. He rushed from the people and ran outside. The jackal called again, but because the dog did not want the people to know they were related, he answered the jackal, "You! We are not related. We are not of the same family. We have separated, so go away. I won't go from here, go away!"

"What does he mean?" asked the jackal to himself. "Does he not want to know me?" He turned to go back into the forest. What could he do?

The next day, the jackal stayed alone, and could catch nothing to eat without the help of his brother. The second night, he went to the same place near the village and called for his brother. The dog answered in the same way as previously, so the jackal decided to return to the forest and give up hope of his brother's return.

The dog stayed in the village, and soon forgot entirely about the other animals in the forest. The people also became used to the dog and they remained friends.

Now, when a dog hears the jackal calling, he repeats the same words, that he will never return to the forest again.

By David Mbaluka
Shimo La Tewa High School, Mombasa
Picture by Kenneth Cainan Orlale
Lenana School

THE CHAMELEON AND THE EAGLE

Long ago, the King of Animals had a very beautiful daughter whom all male animals wanted to marry as their wife. The King didn't want to show favour and so he decided that a competition had to be held. The animals were told that they had to compete in running and the winner would marry the King's daughter.

The eagle was very proud and happy because he thought he would win by flying. The chameleon was very sad because he knew he was slow and did not have a hope.

However, the chameleon was clever and decided to try a trick to win the King's daughter.

When they were about to start running, the chameleon quietly sat on the eagle's tail and since he was light, the eagle could not feel the chameleon on his back.

They started off and the eagle flew proudly, thinking he would reach the finishing line first. He flew and flew and thought there was no doubt that he would win.

When he reached the finishing point of the race and was just about to sit down and relax, the chameleon dropped from his back and shouted, "Don't sit on me!" The eagle was annoyed and said he arrived there first but the fact was that the chameleon had reached the chair before any other animal. The eagle was so furious that he couldn't agree that he had been defeated. They repeated the competition but the very same thing happened again, so the eagle gave up and the King's daughter was married by the chameleon. And there ends my folk story which shows that cleverness can make up for a handicap.

By Alice Githui
Nairobi Girls' Secondary School
Picture by Elizabeth Ocholla
Highlands School, Eldoret

A TRADITIONAL STORY OF THE HAWK AND THE HEN

There are many traditional stories about birds and animals in our
community. Most of these stories are not written down in books, but are
passed from mouth to mouth. Young boys and girls usually hear these
stories from their grandmothers. The stories are mainly told at night
when the children collect together to spend their nights in grandmothers'
houses, as is the custom.

One night when we had all settled on our mats to begin our sleep,
Grandmother decided to tell us a story. Her approach was unique. "Have
you ever stopped to think why the hawk is always pestering the chicken?
Have you seen that even a very young chick is always busy scratching
the ground?" The two questions did not appear difficult to us. We gave
very ready answers which we thought were as convincing as they were
brief.

We told her that both were looking for food. She only laughed and we
knew from her laughter that we had failed the test. "Here is the story,"
said Grandmother.

A long time ago, the hawk and the hen
lived together. Neither of them could fly. They walked or ran on their two legs as
the hen still does today. They were very close friends.

But it happened one day that the hawk picked up a needle-like instrument called
'riwi'. He used this small thing to help him make wings for himself. He neatly sewed

the feathers and when he flapped his wings he found that he could fly. He flew for a short distance and came down again, fearing that he would fall. It was not until after the third trial that he came to believe that he could fly. He flew very proudly over the hen, who remained puzzled and could not believe what she was seeing. Finally, the hawk told her the whole story of how he got his wings.

"Do you know what happened next?" Grandmother asked us. We all chorused our answer, "No!"

"Then listen, don't sleep," she replied.

The hen asked the hawk to give her the riwi, so that she could also make wings. Although they were friends, the hawk was reluctant to lend his wonderful tool. He said that he suspected the hen would easily lose it, and would create enmity between them, and yet he was not ready for a quarrel. The hen pleaded with him further, until he could no longer refuse. She promised that she would never lose it. The hawk, fearing to disappoint his friend, decided to give the hen his magic needle.

She took it happily and dashed away with it. As soon as she was out of sight, she started to work on her wings. But before she finished her work, the needle dropped. She looked for it, but after searching everywhere could not find it. Due to her half-completed wings, the hen found that she could only fly for a short distance. She could not complete her work, having lost the needle.

The next day, the hawk came to ask for his needle. It took the hen some minutes before she could give an answer. However, she at last uttered, "I lost it."

The hawk thought this a joke and could not really believe her. But when it turned out to be the truth, the hawk cried. He told the hen that he must have the needle he

had given her. The hen asked if he would accept any other kind of payment, but he refused.

The hawk told the hen that until she found the needle, they would remain enemies. "Wherever I find your children or you, I will take either of you for my food. I will not stop doing this until you shall have given me my riwi," he said.

Nowadays, chickens are always scratching the soil, turning the leaves or rubbish, trying to find the needle. The hawk, on the other hand, has not forgotten to come and ask for his needle.

Everytime I see a hawk around, it reminds me of this story and whenever it carries away a chicken I always tend to think it is justified in a way. What one wonders is whether the hen will ever find the needle and give it back to the hawk. But if you watch a hen at work you will see that she is trying very hard and may find it one day.

By David Magoma
Agoro Sare High School. Kisii
Picture by Florence Gitau
Kahuhia Girls' School

THE GREEDY
HYENA

"Wildlife not only holds an interest for us as wild game, but has a deeper and maybe a much closer relationship to us. This goes back to the early times when the families used to gather around and the old folks would keep the younger folks busy with animal stories. Then the children would get inspired and stay awake until supper was ready. They sat together in the evening and listened to these stories, some of them being retold the tenth time but never losing interest. There were many such stories and here is one of those old accounts."

The hyena had not had anything to chew or break with his carnivore's teeth. He had yawned the whole night waiting hopefully for the dawn to appear.

As the dawn appeared, the hyena was already walking sluggishly in the bushes, his nose raised high in the air. By now, the rays of the sun had penetrated through the cool soil and had started heating it. The heat of the sun seems to waken everything asleep on the earth, for it was not long after the hyena had been wandering aimlessly in the bush that he smelled something. He carried his unwilling legs towards the origin of the smell. It did not take him long before he came to an abrupt standstill. Just in front of him was a big heap of sand, and on one side was a very huge block of rock. The hyena suddenly recognized this as a grave. From this heap of sand came an appetising smell. By now, saliva had started to flow down his tongue as juice comes out of a squeezed fruit.

As the hyena started to dislodge the soil he did not notice that he gave the stone less stability. He worked with great zeal knowing that this was his day. The faster the hyena worked, the more saliva poured down like water from his mouth. This was because he was hungry and was anxious to have his jaws grinding over one another. Despite the heavy work which was in front of him the hyena never gave up.

It so happened that as the squirrel was going home in the evening, he heard a squeal. At first he thought it to be a sound sometimes made by lovers, and he concluded that it was some lovers enjoying their honeymoon. Anyway, he decided to go and have a look, and to his amazement found his friend the hyena trapped by a huge rock.

The hyena tried to gasp something out of his mouth, which was sealed by the soil,

but nothing audible came out. The squirrel knew at once that his friend wanted some help. And so the squirrel got to work. He worked with so much enthusiasm that before dusk the block of rock was lying beside his tormented friend. As the exhausted squirrel sat down after this hard work, the hyena crawled out of the pit and instantly grabbed the squirrel. He threatened the squirrel by saying that he was going to make a supper out of him.

Just at the time this quarrel was going on the rabbit happened to be passing by, and the squirrel called him to come and settle the case. The rabbit said that such a case was a difficult one, and unless they started the whole thing again, he could not judge it. So the hyena went back to the pit and the stone was rolled back. In this way, the rabbit said, he was not going to have prejudice towards or against either of them.

As the hyena and the squirrel waited for the case to start, the case was already ending, for the rabbit said, "You squirrel, go on your way as you came, and you hyena, stay as the squirrel found you." Therefore the squirrel went on his own, and the hyena was left to suffer under that huge block of stone, thus ending the dispute between the two of them.

The hyena spent the whole night there and it was only by good luck that the elephant happened to be passing near by the following morning. By the time the hyena was rescued, he was weak and worn out. His hindlimbs were affected most, which is why we find them today shorter than the forelimbs.

By James Nduati
Pumwani Secondary School
Picture by John Kimunya
Ofafa Jericho Secondary School

WHY THE ELEPHANT IS SO BIG

Once the elephant was not as big as it is today but was the same size as other animals. But it became so rude that the "Board of Governors" decided to do something about it. The small animals liked the idea of having the rude elephant out of the way very much. The Board decided that they should beat the animal until it was lame. The idea brought much excitement such that most of them were nearly bursting when they reached home, and they started the big act of sharpening their weapons.

They appointed the day for the punishment of the elephant. The ant lived alone in his house, so having taken his sword he called his friend the louse to tighten it around his waist. The ant was so determined to fight the elephant that he could not stand to lose the sword during the fight, so he urged his friend to tighten more. The louse did not want to annoy his friend, so he continued.

"More.... more.... oh!!" At last there was nothing of the tummy of the ant. Seeing this the louse laughed.... laughed without measure so that his nose dropped off! This incident explains the absence of a nose in the louse and stomach in the ant.

However, they both recovered from their shock and proceeded to the battle-field. They all gave the elephant a beating but being a young healthy male, he fought back. In the course of the fight, he managed to catch the giraffe by the neck (until then the giraffe had a normal neck and was considered holy). The other animals decided to rescue their friend and a tug-of-war started which they eventually won.

The elephant was badly hurt, but after visiting the witch-doctor he began to heal, although his swollen body never returned to its smaller size. Also, the giraffe, after some tender care, got well, but his neck remained long.

Thus, in this short story we find how four of the animals came to be as we see them today. Are they pass-the-night stories or are they true?

By Alex Nganga
Nanyuki Secondary School
Picture by Rachel Nafwa
Highlands School, Eldoret

WHY THE GIRAFFE CAN'T SPEAK

Once upon a time when animal language was spoken everywhere in the forest, the giraffe, because of his long neck was able to boast of being the King of the Animals. Taller than all the other animals, he would look up into the sky and break into long, loving conversations with himself. As a result, all the other animals soon became very annoyed with the giraffe, as he deprived them of their afternoon peace and quiet.

As time went on, the animals began to think of a way in which they could silence the giraffe. One day, the leopard went to the giraffe and said, "You are praising yourself for nothing, because you cannot do as many things as the other animals can."

At this, the giraffe became very angry and annoyed and shouted at the leopard to tell him one of the things which he couldn't do. The leopard told the giraffe that he couldn't even run as fast as him. The giraffe only mocked him and then agreed with the leopard to have a race and see who would reach their destination first.

The race was to be held soon and the leopard, who was absolutely sure that he would be the winner, went and told all the other animals about this race. The other animals, who were in favour of the leopard, were very excited to hear this and they went to watch the race, full of hope that the leopard would win.

The race started and both leopard and giraffe ran as fast as they could, but very unluckily the leopard banged into a tree and was wounded badly, while he was rounding a corner. The other animals' hearts sank to see this, the giraffe won the race and he began to praise himself more than ever.

By this time, all the animals were very angry. After several days, the monkey, who was a clever animal, thought of a way to silence the giraffe.

He collected some gum from the trees and stuck it on the leaves of the trees, which the giraffe usually ate. He then waited for the giraffe to come and eat these leaves. The giraffe soon came and began to eat.

Then a lovely thing happened. The leaves stuck in the long neck of the giraffe and when he tried to speak he just couldn't. The other animals were very glad to see this, and they thanked the monkey very much for his wonderful deed.

And so, from that day onwards the giraffe became dumb. This is a legend which was related to me when I was a little girl.

By Yasmin Lalji
Highlands School, Eldoret
Picture by Rosaline Siman
Highlands School, Eldoret

HOW THE
TORTOISE GOT CRACKS
ON ITS SHELL

A long time ago, when there was a big famine everywhere, all the birds were asked to attend a feast up in the sky, being given by their King.

When the tortoise heard that all the birds were going to a feast in the sky, he had moments of sadness and depression, for he wished that he was a bird too, so that he could attend the feast. He sat down in his house, and thought about what to do. He had hardly eaten anything worthwhile for two weeks, and he had no means of getting any food, because the sun had scorched every bit of green plant in the land.

At last, he knew what to do; he approached all the birds and told them that, although he was not a bird he wanted to go with them to that great feast, and that they should help him. He said, "As you do a favour for somebody, tomorrow it's his turn to pay you all the kindness you did to him."

So all birds agreed to the tortoise's request, and each contributed a feather to the tortoise, until he had two full wings, like the birds. His wings were exceedingly beautiful, because each feather was of a different kind. His heart sang with joy to have succeeded in going to the feast. He knew that there would be some drinks, meat and other dishes of food to eat.

The feast day came, and all birds and the tortoise left their homes to go to the King's palace in the sky. When they reached half-way the tortoise told all birds that it was not good to be called by their usual names when attending a big meeting or feast. He said "Everyone should choose a new name for himself." They all agreed, and the tortoise chose the name, "ALL OF YOU."

When they arrived, the King saw that the tortoise was a person of dignity and rank.

Picture on previous page

And when the feast started, the tortoise was chosen as the speaker. His speech was so eloquent that everyone liked it. After the speech, meals were served, and they were brought a dish and some drinks.

The servant said to them, "This meal is for all of you," and then went away.

When they were about to start eating, the tortoise said, "You remember that we chose new names on the way. And you all know that my new name is 'ALL OF YOU', and the servant said the food is for 'all of you', which means it's mine. So you can leave me alone."

So he was left alone, and ate whatever was there for himself. The birds became angry and agreed to take back their feathers. They flew home with empty stomachs.

The tortoise was going to be stranded in the sky with no feathers. So he sent a message to his wife, that she should take all the soft things from the house and put them out in front, because he was going to fall. But when the bird with the message reached Earth, he told the tortoise's wife to put all the hardest things on the ground.

When the tortoise looked down, he saw things put in front of his house and thought that everything was all right. So he let himself fall.

The voyage in the air seemed very long. When he reached the ground, he fell badly, and his shell was severely broken, because of the rough things put out by his wife.

That is why a tortoise has its shell cracked in many places up to this day.

By Mwadebwe Saidi
Shimo La Tewa High School, Mombasa
Picture by Joseph Ngware
Cardinal Otunga Secondary School

WHY
LIONS ROAR

A very long time ago, when the world was just beginning, the lion used to make a crying noise like that of a sheep; so he had as many animals as he wanted for his meals. He was the King of all the animals, and although the small ones like the hare ("Nyagithin") did not like the idea, they had no one to take their complaints to.

The animals called very many meetings, but none of these helped in any way. One day the leopard said a new meeting should be called. It was done, and he told the others that it was only a matter of tricking the lion.

"Well," said the leopard, "Is there anybody who is ready to do the trick?" Nobody spoke. Saying is always easy, but doing is a real problem.

Nyagithin (the hare), whose only remaining relative had just been eaten, sat under a tree thinking of what he could do to this creature. After a short silence, he said "Aaaa!!! 'Sibuor' (lion) thinks I'm too small but he is wrong. I can defeat him." He stood up immediately and spread the news to others. He told them that he had thought of a way to trick their greedy King. Others like the elephant laughed at Nyagithin, but this only gave him more courage.

At a meeting the next day, Nyagithin stood up and proclaimed, "There is not a minute to waste, as you all know the problem and the worries of every animal here. I have therefore decided to bring my own wisdom to this. You all know that wisdom is better than strength, so wish me good luck and don't be impatient, comrades. I'm off!"

Nyagithin went to a bee-hive which he had noticed sometime back, and collected all the honey. He ate as much as he wanted, put some in a bottle, covered it and took the rest to the King.

When he arrived at the lion's den, the lion's family were so happy because they thought that Nyagithin had come to be eaten. Before he could reach the King, he was seen from afar and given a chorus of greetings. Nyagithin told the lion that he had some honey for him in the forest and that he should follow him if he was interested in having some of it. The lion agreed very quickly. Nyagithin then led the way to the forest. When they arrived Nyagithin said, "My master, I have been sent

by other animals to offer you this," showing him the honey in the bottle, and pretending it was oil. "I have also offered you honey and here it is." The greedy king began eating as quickly as he could.

At last Nyagithin told him that the other animals had said he was to be smeared with the oil in the bottle. The lion agreed so Nyagithin smeared his whole body and told him it was all finished. He then left the lion sleeping under the tree, went to the river and washed himself. After this, he went to the other animals and sat down to rest. The other animals moved near him and tried to talk to him, but Nyagithin only told them to wait and hear with their own ears.

The lion, who was left under the tree, was by this time fast asleep and snoring so loudly that the other animals could hear him from very far. When the bees came from their journey, they found that all their honey had been stolen. They immediately began searching for the thief. After a short time they met the lion sleeping under the tree. It was the smell which came from the lion which made them go to him. They did not waste any time asking him where he had found the honey. They all stung him at once. He tried to explain, but they were too angry to listen to him. He tried to tell them that it had been a present, but they had no time to listen to the lion who by this time had discovered the trick which Nyagithin had played on him.

In the end he began roaring! The little bees were frightened by this noise and flew for their lives. After this the lion began searching for Nyagithin planning to punish him severely, but not knowing that he would never catch him or any other animal.

He tried to stop roaring but he could not. The other animals, who did not know where the noise was coming from, were so frightened and thought that perhaps the world was coming to an end. Nyagithin only laughed at them and told them that it was the lion—so Nyagithin had succeeded in tricking the lion. He told them that they had to run whenever they heard that kind of noise.

The lion became annoyed and hungry, but he could get no revenge. Up to this very day lions roar, and whenever they are heard other animals must run for their lives.

"Tinda" thus ends the story.

By Emily A. Orondo
Highlands School, Eldoret
Picture by Mary Kariuki
Tumu Tumu Girls' School

THE
HEDGEHOG AND
THE HARE

Animal legends have been told for many centuries. Some are still being told nowadays. This story is about the hedgehog and the hare, and comes from South Maragoli.

One bright sunny morning, a little hedgehog was sitting at the door of his home. He was a merry little fellow, who wished everybody to be happy. "I think I will just run over the field and take a look at the turnips," he said to his wife.

"I hope you won't meet any of those rude hares," said Mrs. Hedgehog. "Yesterday, two of them came to the cabbage patch when our little ones and I were there. They laughed loudly at our short stumpy legs, and said that it must be terrible to be slow."

"Do not worry about them," said her husband. "A hedgehog is as good as a hare any day. Goodbye, I will be back soon."

Just as Mr. Hedgehog reached the turnip field, he met a big bouncing hare on his way to the cabbage patch. This hare was proud, and thought himself a very fine fellow indeed, because he could run like the wind.

When the hedgehog saw the hare, he said in his best manner, "Good morning, Mr. Hare!" The hare did not answer this polite greeting, but said in a rude, rough voice, "Why are you out so early this morning?"

"I am just taking a nice short walk for a breath of fresh air," replied the hedgehog.

"How can you enjoy a walk with such queer short legs?" asked the hare. "By the way, I saw your wife and little ones yesterday. They were trying to run races, but not one of them could run faster than a tortoise. I nearly died laughing at them!"

These rude remarks made the hedgehog very angry. "I suppose you think your long legs are better than my short ones," he said. "If you are not afraid, I will run a race with you."

"You! Swifter than I am!" said the hare with a laugh. "We will settle this matter at once. We will race down the furrows between these fine turnips. You run in one furrow, and I'll run in another. We shall see who reaches the other end first!"

"I will not race with you just now," said the hedgehog. "I am very hungry and must go home for breakfast. I'll be back in half-an-hour." So the hare said he would wait for him, and the hedgehog went off home.

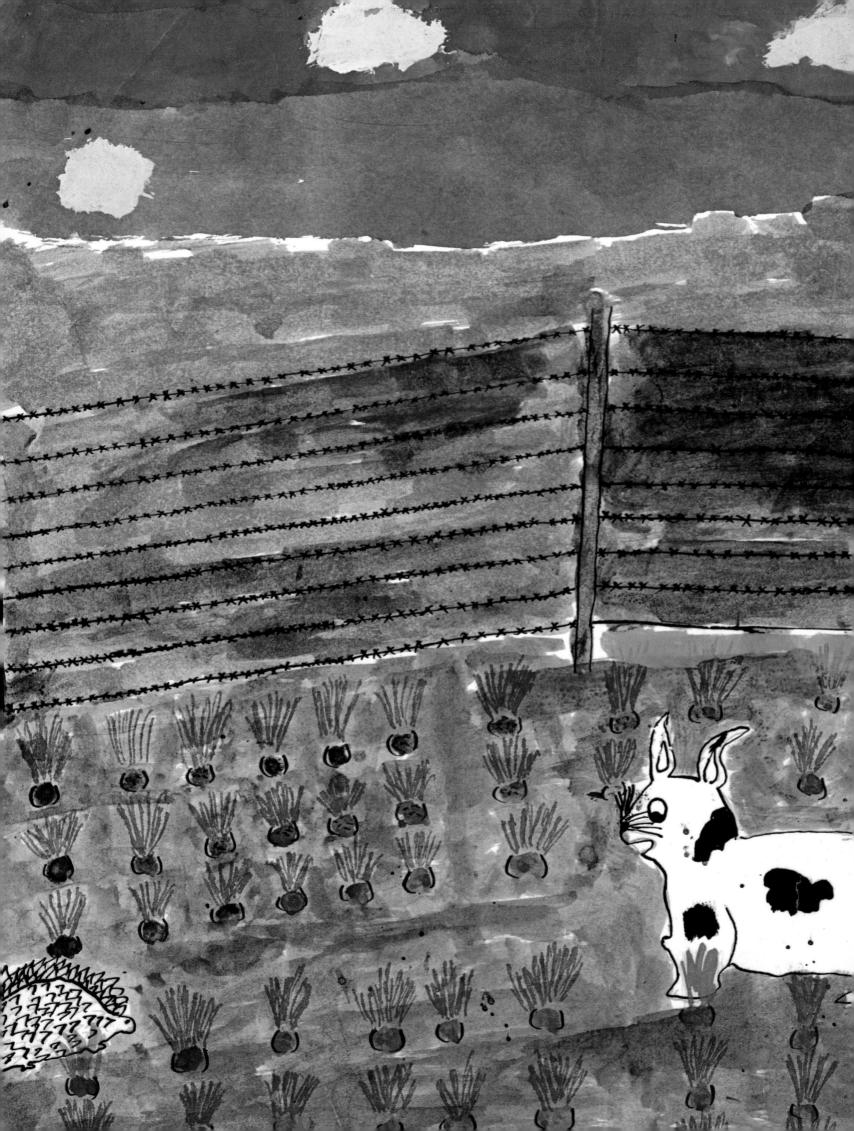

"That rude hare is far too proud," said the hedgehog to himself. "I'll teach him not to be so boastful."

When he reached home, the little hedgehog asked his wife to help play a trick on the hare. "Here is my plan," he said. "You and I look so much alike that the hare cannot tell the difference between us. You hide at the far end of the furrow, and just before the hare reaches you, pop your head up and say, 'I knew I could beat you quite easily'."

Soon they reached the field and the hedgehog placed his wife at the far end of the furrow. Then he went to the other end, where he found the hare waiting for him. "Let us start at once," said the hare. "I am now quite ready," said the little hedgehog, as he took his furrow.

The hare hopped into the next furrow and took his place. Then he called, "Ready, steady, go!" and off he ran like the wind. The little hedgehog ran only a few steps and then lay still among the leaves.

Just before the hare reached the far end of the furrow, the hedgehog's wife popped up her head and said, "I knew I could beat you quite easily!"

The hare stood and said, "Let's try the second time." At the other end was Mr. Hedgehog, who popped out his head and cried, "Again, I have beaten you!"

They tried again for the third and fourth time, but Mr. Hare was beaten by the hedgehog. So Mr. Hedgehog told the hare to let that be a lesson. Now the hare was very tired and could not run any more, and so hopped home slowly and sadly, crying all the way.

The two little hedgehogs laughed and laughed. "Brains are far better than legs," said Mr. Hedgehog to his happy wife. "Mr Hare will not be so proud the next time we meet him."

By Winnie Makungu Ombeva
Nairobi Girls' School
Picture by Lucy Hoareau
Limuru Girls' School

WHY THE HYRAX IS MISSING A TAIL

When the Creator made all the animals, he did not complete the job all at once. They were to be given tails later.

All the animals were told to report back on a certain date, and when the day was near, they happily prepared themselves.

On the big day, Mr. Hyrax, a very small animal, was not worried, thinking that "Being a small animal, I will sleep until just a few hours before the tails are given out." The day was as cold as ice and completely clear. So Mr. Hyrax slept. Later, he awoke and took his time washing, brushing himself, and eating. Then he began his journey to where the tails were being handed out.

On the way he walked proudly, singing to himself. By and by, he started meeting some other animals who had already been awarded their tails, and in fact, very beautiful ones.

When he finally reached the place, the Creator told him that the tails were finished. On hearing this, Mr. Hyrax was perturbed and ashamed. He regretted all the time he had wasted sleeping. The other animals were now very happy and they laughed at him. He could not tolerate their laughter, so he went home. At home, his problems continued when he saw his friends with tails, while he had nothing. Therefore, he decided to run to the rocks and hide. This is why hyraxes are found today on rocks and around trees.

This is a Kamba folk story.

By Master Kimatu
Shimo La Tewa School, Mombasa
Picture by Faith Munuke
Limuru Girls' School

THE KITE
AND
THE HYENAS

Long ago there were very many hyenas in my country. They ate people every night and soon they decided that the people were not fat enough, and they wanted a change.

All along they had wondered what made the white clouds in the sky. It was the kite who solved this problem. One day as the kite was just about to fly up to the upper atmosphere, the hyenas called him to them, wanting to speak to him. When the kite came, the hyenas asked him. "Good Mr. Kite, can you tell us what that white stuff in the sky is?"

The kite was very delighted at the question, and he answered, "Good friends, those are called white clouds and they are made of nothing but fat. No one can reach them except myself and that's where I am going this very minute."

When the hyenas heard the mention of fat, the saliva started dripping down their chins. They pleaded with the kite that he should take them there to eat some of the fat because they had missed fat meat terribly.

The kite was very pleased because he knew that his chance to do away with hyenas had come at last. He thought for some time and said, "I will not take you because you eat all the dead bodies and leave nothing for me. Unless you promise that you will be leaving me some meat in future, I will not grant your request."

All the hyenas gave their promise and the kite agreed to take them to the clouds to eat some fat. The hyenas had already decided among themselves that once they got there, nothing would ever make them leave the fat and come down to earth again.

The kite gave them a command that one of them should cling to his quill feathers and the rest should hold on to each other's tail. This was very quickly done. All the hyenas were ready to go to that distant land of fat where they could live for ever. They sung and danced to all the steps.

But there was a poor, broken-legged hyena who was left behind because the others would have nothing to do with him.

The kite took to flight. Up and up he flew with a long 'chain' of hyenas singing and talking behind him. The hyenas looked down, but all they could see was darkness. The sick hyena left behind was very unhappy. He wept as if his heart would break.

When the kite could no longer see the earth, he told the hyenas to stop singing their song, and he told them, "Suppose I tell my feathers to come off, what would you do?"

The hyenas held their breath and asked the kite not to do such a thing. But the kite was bent on finishing the job. So he said, "The feathers of Mr. Kite, come off! I shall grow new ones."

Then the feathers came off and down went the hyenas. Their singing and talking had turned to crying. They all wished for different things, such as, "I wish I could fall in the sea"; I wish I could fall in the mud"; "I wish I could fall on top of a tree."

Despite their wishes, they all died except the one left behind with the broken leg—which lived to be the mother of the hyenas there are today.

That is why hyenas of today limp, and do not eat people live. To show gratitude to Mr. Kite, people named him "Chill the Kite", which means "the intelligent kite".

By Amos Kandie
Kenyatta University College
Picture by Rosa Ndeti
Limuru Girls' School

THE CLEVERNESS
OF
THE HARE

Once when there was a very heavy drought, the animals all suffered from lack of food and water. King Lion decreed that all animals should bring their tools and build a dam to hold the next rains.

The animals worked until they could hardly stand up, but they finished the dam, which eventually did fill up with water.

The only animal who had shirked his share of the hard labour was the tricky Hare. Therefore, the King declared that the dam would be guarded night and day to prevent the Hare from drinking. The first on guard was the Pig. Hare deceived him easily by tempting him with a cowrie full of honey. While the Pig's eyes were shut and his mouth open to receive the honey, the Hare filled his gourd with water and ran off. The next guard was the Hyena and the Hare fooled him in the same way and took more water.

Next, the Tortoise claimed that he thought he could guard the dam more successfully, so the King gave him a chance to try.

Tortoise covered his body with a sticky substance and submerged himself under water. When Hare came and saw no one, he started to fetch water, but gradually he became stuck to the sticky Tortoise who was hiding under the water's surface. The Hare was caught.

King Lion wanted to eat Hare on the spot, and the animals all agreed to this. But Hare persuaded them that he would taste better if they cooked him first. He said they should swing him in a circle over the fire. The foolish animals agreed to this, but of course when they swung him in the direction of the fire and let go, the agile Hare bounded away. He had outwitted them again, and once more escaped his punishment.

By Johnny B. Futtuh
Shimo La Tewa Secondary School, Mombasa
Picture by John Njoroge
Langata High School

THE ELEPHANT
AND
THE HIPPO

Once upon a time the Cunning Rabbit set out to challenge the Elephant and the Hippo. At that time they were really dear friends and never dreamt of picking a quarrel with each other. But the Rabbit saw them as two giants in the Fauna Kingdom with whom he could make wonderful sport.

One day the Rabbit visited the Elephant and began to say, "Despite your mighty nature, I'm confident that I can win a tug-of-war with you, Elephant." This sent a current of terror through the Elephant. At last the Elephant said, "To prove your nonsense impossible, a day shall be fixed so that you meet your fate." The Rabbit wagged his tail and fixed a date.

As long as the day remained to come, the Rabbit lived an innocent but impatient life. During this critical time, he went to see the Hippo and also challenged him to a tug-of-war. The Rabbit categorically stated that he, himself, would be the hero. Although this amused the Hippo at first, in the end an agreement was reached and the same date was set.

On the day agreed the Rabbit rushed forth to the Elephant and said, "The great day has come and you would be a woman to stay at home. I have brought a rope to which I shall tie you and I shall hold the other end." The Rabbit continued, "When

I tap the rope you will know that I am ready and you should start to pull."

Having tied the Elephant, the Rabbit moved with the rest of the rope to the river to tie the Hippo. At this height of his mischief, the Rabbit had been able to connect the Elephant and the Hippo without their knowledge. He ran and tapped the rope and the giant mammals began to pull against each other. Each animal tried his best to disprove the Rabbit. Of course, the rope could not resist the friction and broke, so the Elephant had a mighty fall and the Hippo fell back into the river.

To the Elephant this was a disgrace because his power had done nothing. He was so angered that he rose and started to bark and uproot any tree that came in his way with the hope of finding the Rabbit. But till today, the Elephant has never set an eye on the Rabbit at close quarters and his hunt continues.

As for the Hippo, he had such a terrible fright that he vowed never to come out of the water during the day lest he meet with the "Mighty Rabbit". Till now, the Hippo only comes out under the cover of night.

By Richard Wanjala
Shimo La Tewa School, Mombasa
Picture by Jackton Lusi
The Rift Valley Technical School, Eldoret

WHY BATS FACE DOWNWARDS

On one Christmas day three creatures —a bat, a quail and a mouse—sat down together to decide how they could celebrate. They decided to buy a cow.

As it was on a Market Day, they contributed some amount of money and went to the market. They bought a very fat, middle-aged cow, and a rope for tying it. Their homes were far off, and before they could reach them it started to rain very heavily.

As it was raining so much, they decided to tie the cow in the bush where no one could get it and they went to a nearby village for a drink.

When the rain had stopped, they went back to take the cow, so they could get home to where more creatures were waiting for the celebration.

But when they reached the place where the cow was tied, they found only half of the rope still tied to the tree—and the other half gone together with the cow.

After finding that the cow was gone, they tried to think of what to do, but could not come to a firm decision.

Then Mr. Bat suggested that they should go back to the market and check to see if the cow had returned there. They all agreed, and did this, but all was in vain. After a long search they could not find it.

These three creatures then all made promises amongst themselves. Mr. Mouse promised that, since the cow must have followed one of the roads, he would never cross the road again, and even today, if a mouse crosses any road, then it dies just on the spot.

Mr. Quail promised that he would not sit on any tree, because it was the tree which allowed the cow to go. Up till now, quails do not sit on any trees at all.

And Mr. Bat promised that, because it was Heaven that rain came from and the rain made them leave the cow, he would never again look upwards. You can see this for yourself—that bats always face downwards, even when they are flying in the air.

By Joseck Akungu
Agoro Sare High School, Kisii
Picture by Julie Aliker
Limuru Girls' School

HOW "ONGO-WANG", THE CROWN BIRD, GOT ITS NAME

Of all the birds that I know by name in our language, none has
achieved such an appropriate name as the one called "Ongo-wang."
Of course, there might be legends in other tribes as to the origin of the
name but I am fully convinced that the way our tribe relates the story of
how the bird got its name is the most suitable one.
Now the question is why and how the bird became called Ongo-wang,
as the word "ongo" means *eagle*, and the other word, "wang", in this
sense means *burning*; so if the name could be translated from our
language into English the name would be "Eagle is burning" instead of
Crown Bird.
Now this is the story of how the bird acquired the name we now use.

Long ago when animals used to hold
celebrations the birds held one to celebrate their victory over other animals which,
although bigger than them, could not fly. The legend says that towards the end of
the feast the birds came together to take their final meal, as is the custom in our
society. Food was there in plenty and every bird ate and drank as much as it could.

In the evening the main part of the celebration was over and the birds merely
chatted to pass the time, commenting on the events of the great day. While this was
going on, a bird called "Ongo," the eagle, suggested that a piece of meat should be
roasted and left over the fire so that a race could be held to get the meat off the fire.
It was agreed that they would start some distance away and the winner would of
course get the meat. All the birds agreed as they were eager to see what would happen
to the winner of such a risky game. I am sure you know how fond eagles are of meat,
and of course the eagle was sure of winning the game even though there were many
swifter birds there. Soon the distance to be raced over was agreed upon and the fire
was lit at the other end of the course and the piece of meat began to cook.

The birds gathered at the starting line facing the fire with the piece of meat roasting
gently on it. The race began, each bird hoping to win the meat. Of course all the

birds flew as fast as they could and the dove and swift reached the fire first but shot past as they feared the flames. However, Ongo came swooping down and grasped the piece of meat, but he also caught on to some pieces of burning wood. Now, remember birds are covered in feathers—and how do feathers and fire react when brought together? Of course this is what happened to the eagle, who was covered in feathers, and soon he was on fire.

What about the other birds? They were yelling and jumping in the air, and some began to cry and others even began to laugh. One bird that kept on jumping in the air continued to yell "ongo wang, ongo wang, ongo wang..." This means "the eagle is burning" and from this the bird got its name.

The birds departed and left the eagle burning but the Crown Bird, as it is called in English, never forgot the sight of the burning eagle and so even today he keeps on yelling "Ongo wang, ongo wang"—the eagle is burning!

By Azariah Z. O. Micah
Agoro Sare High School, Kisii
Picture by Eunice Ncharo
Limuru Girls' School